AMAZING MACHINES

KINGFISHER

An imprint of Kingfisher Publications Plc
New Penderel House, 283-288 High Holborn, London WC1V 7HZ
www.kingfisherpub.com

First published in this format 2003
10 9 8 7 6 5 4 3 2 1

The material in this collection was first published by Kingfisher
in four separate volumes:
Dazzling Diggers (1997)
Roaring Rockets (1997)
Flashing Fire Engines (1998)
Terrific Trains (1998)

A CIP catalogue record for this book is available from the British Library.

ISBN 0 7534 0882 1

Printed in China
1TR/0303/TIMS/DOC/128MA

AMAZING MACHINES

Tony Mitton and Ant Parker

KINGFISHER

Contents

Dazzling
DIGGERS

Diggers are noisy, strong and big.

Diggers can carry and push and dig.

Diggers have shovels to scoop and lift,

blades that bulldoze, shunt and shift.

11

Diggers have buckets to gouge out ground,

breakers that crack and smash and pound.

Diggers move rubble and rocks and soil,

so diggers need drinks of diesel oil.

Some have tyres and some have tracks.

Some keep steady with legs called jacks.

Tyres and tracks grip hard as they travel,

squish through mud and grind through gravel.

Diggers go scrunch and squelch and slosh.

This dirty digger needs a hosepipe wash.

Diggers can bash and crash and break,

make things crumble, shiver and shake.

Diggers can heave and hoist and haul.

Diggers help buildings tower up tall.

Diggers park neatly, down on the site.

Then digger-drivers all go home. Goodnight.

Digger bits

levers

these control different parts of the digger

jack

this holds the digger steady when it is lifting or digging

blade

this is for knocking down and pushing along

tyre

this helps the wheel to grip the ground and get the digger moving

breaker

this is for cracking concrete or lumps of rock

bucket

this is for digging and scooping out

piston

this is a strong pump that makes parts of the digger move about

tracks

these help the digger to travel over slippery or bumpy ground

Roaring ROCKETS

Rockets have power. They rise and roar.

This rocket's waiting, ready to soar.

Rockets carry astronauts with cool, white suits.

oxygen helmets and gravity boots.

The countdown is finishing: 3, 2, 1 . . .

Action! Blast off! The journey's begun.

Rockets have fuel in great big tanks.

When they're empty, they drop away…thanks!

Up in space you're really light,

so astronauts strap themselves in tight.

Rockets explore. Through space they zoom,

reaching as far as the big, round moon.

Out comes the lander with legs out ready

and fiery boosters to hold it steady.

Rockets take astronauts out to a place

that's strange and wonderful: silent space...

Moon mission over, the lander's left outside.

We're back in the rocket for the long return ride.

Rockets re-enter in a fiery flash
to land at sea with a sizzling splash!

48

The helicopter carries the brave crew away.
Let's give them a cheer. Hip, hip, hooray!

Rocket bits

gravity boots

gravity keeps us on the ground but there is not a lot on the moon so boots are worn that grip the ground and stop you floating off

lunar lander

Lunar lander

this takes astronauts down from the rocket to land on the moon

oxygen helmet

we need to breathe oxygen but there is none in space, so astronauts carry their own supply which flows into their helmets

fuel tanks

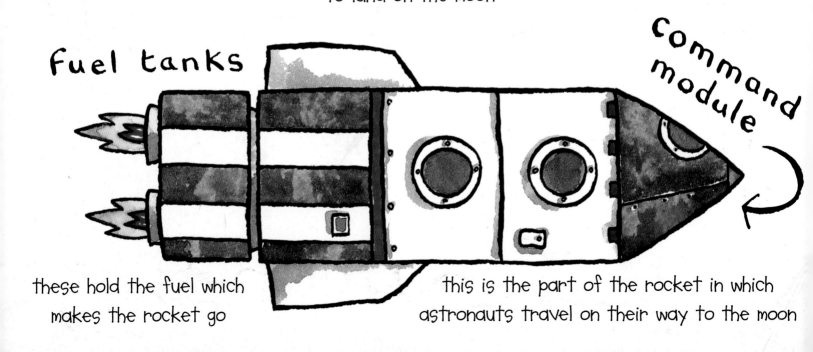

command module

these hold the fuel which makes the rocket go

this is the part of the rocket in which astronauts travel on their way to the moon

Flashing
FIRE ENGINES

Big, bold fire engines, waiting day and night,

ready for a rescue or a blazing fire to fight.

As soon as there's a fire alarm,
the engine starts to roar.

54

The firefighters jump aboard –
it rumbles out the door.

Watch the engine speeding, on its daring dash.

Hear its siren screaming. See its bright lights flash.

In helmets, fireproof coats and trousers,
boots so big and strong,

the crew are dressed and ready
as the engine zooms along.

When the engine finds the fire,
it quickly pulls up near.

The crew jump out, unroll the hose
and get out all the gear.

The hose has got a nozzle
that shoots a jet of spray.
It squirts right at the blazing flames
and sizzles them away.

The water tank is empty soon,
so where can more be found?
The engine's pump can pull it up
from pipes below the ground.

The fire is hot and roaring.
It makes a lot of smoke.

The firefighters put on masks,
otherwise they'd choke.

The ladder rises upward. It reaches for the sky.
A fire engine's ladder stretches up so very high!

66

Sometimes there's a platform, right up at the top.
t waits beside the window. Then into it you hop.

67

At last the fire's extinguished.
The flames are all put out.

plop!

plop!

Lower the ladder. Roll the hose.
"Hooray!" the fire crew shout.

Back inside the station,
the crew can take a break.

But the fire engine's ready
and it's waiting wide-awake.

Fire Engine bits

helmet

this is a hard hat that protects the firefighter's head

fireproof coats and trousers

these are made from special material that does not burn easily and protects firefighters from the fire

masks and tank

we cannot breathe in smoky air so firefighters carry clean air in **tanks** on their backs and this flows into their **masks**

siren

this makes a loud noise to tell people to move out of the way and let the fire engine pass

water tank

this is inside the middle of the fire engine and holds water to fight the fire – some fire engines carry foam, too

pump

this sucks water from the tank and pushes it out through tubes called **hoses** – it also gets water from underground through big taps in the street called **hydrants**

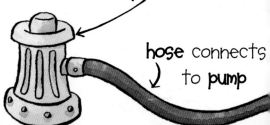

hose connects to **pump**

Terrific
TRAINS

Big trains, small trains, old trains and new,

rattling and whistling – choo, choo, choo!

Starting from the station with a whistle and a hiss

steam trains puffing and chuffing like this.

Diesel trains rushing as they rattle down the line,

varning us they're coming with a long, low whine.

Metal wheels whirl as they whizz along the track.
They shimmer and they swish
with a slick click-clack.

Carriages are coupled in a neat, long chain.
An engine pulls the carriages,
and that makes a train.

81

If a train meets a river or a valley or a ridge,

the train goes over on a big, strong bridge.

If a train meets a mountain it doesn't have to stop

It travels through a tunnel and your ears go pop!

When too many trains try to share the same track.

the signals and the points have to hold some back.

When the rail meets a road,
there's a crossing with a gate.

The train rushes through
while the traffic has to wait.

Trains travel anytime, even very late.

This train's delivering a big load of freight.

This train's for passengers.
We'll soon be on our way.

All aboard and wave goodbye—
we're off on holiday!

Train bits

rails

electric rail

these are metal strips that form a pathway called a **track** or **railway line** – some trains get their power from an electric rail

whistle

this makes a noise to warn everyone that the train is coming

wagon

this is for carrying goods, called **freight**

signal

this tells train drivers when to stop and go

carriage

this is for carrying people, called **passengers**

points

these are rails that move to let the railway line divide so the train changes direction

Collect more
AMAZING MACHINES

Amazing Aeroplanes
Brilliant Boats

Coming soon:
Tough Trucks
Tremendous Tractors